Valér

Living in the semi-arid region

Valéria Fernandes de Oliveira Sousa
Gisele L. dos Santos

Living in the semi-arid region

Drought and salinity studies

ScienciaScripts

Imprint

Any brand names and product names mentioned in this book are subject to trademark, brand or patent protection and are trademarks or registered trademarks of their respective holders. The use of brand names, product names, common names, trade names, product descriptions etc. even without a particular marking in this work is in no way to be construed to mean that such names may be regarded as unrestricted in respect of trademark and brand protection legislation and could thus be used by anyone.

Cover image: www.ingimage.com

This book is a translation from the original published under ISBN 978-613-9-60450-0.

Publisher:
Sciencia Scripts
is a trademark of
Dodo Books Indian Ocean Ltd. and OmniScriptum S.R.L publishing group

120 High Road, East Finchley, London, N2 9ED, United Kingdom
Str. Armeneasca 28/1, office 1, Chisinau MD-2012, Republic of Moldova, Europe

ISBN: 978-620-7-27805-3

CONTENTS

PRESENTATION

This book is a collection of academic papers in Agricultural Sciences with an emphasis on water deficit and salinity, which are abiotic stresses present in semi-arid regions such as the Brazilian Northeast. The book is divided into two chapters, the first on water deficit and the second on salinity in irrigation water. This work was the result of research experiments at the State University of Paraíba, where it is hoped that this work will disseminate the knowledge acquired.

CHAPTER 1

Strategies for the early selection of
drought-resistant sunflower genotypes
for use in family farming in the
Paraíba
hinterland

SUMMARY

The semi-arid northeastern region is ideal for implementing actions that can increase the population's income and development. It is understandable that one of the species that meets this demand is sunflower (*Helianthus annuus* L.). However, abiotic stresses common to the region in question, such as water scarcity, can drastically interfere with the crop's growth and productivity. In order to expand sunflower-growing areas in the Northeast, programmes are needed to obtain and characterise varieties that are more resistant to drought. In this context, this study set out to test the hypothesis that grain production and oil yield in sunflower grown under conditions of water deficiency are dependent on the growing environment and drought resistance and can be seen in the early vegetative stages of the plant's life cycle. To this end, four consecutive and interdependent experiments were carried out under the following headings: (I) Selection of sunflower genotypes adapted to cultivation in a semi-arid environment, where the genotypes Embrapa 122, BRSG01, Helio253, Helio250, BRSG26 were evaluated and the genotypes BRSG01 and Helio253 were defined as the most adapted to cultivation in a semi-arid environment and adopted for the two subsequent experiments; (II) Evaluation of the level of sunflower resistance to drought induced at the germination stage, where aspects of the two genotypes' drought resistance were observed during germination; (III) Evaluation of the level of sunflower resistance to drought induced at the stage of slow vegetative growth of the crop, where the minimum water table necessary for the survival of the two genotypes was defined; Through the evidence taken it can be defined that both genotypes suffered treatment effects. More broadly, the effects are more evident in the form of visual damage. However, they can still be relatively easily detected by analysing the diameter of the stem and the number of leaves. Considering the damage index as a strong indicator of damage, it is suggested that treatment at 20 per cent of field capacity is borderline and that below this the species suffers irreparable damage.

Keywords: agricultural production chains, *Helianthus annuus*, physiological resistance to drought.

1 INTRODUCTION

In the north-eastern region of Brazil, of the 1,600,000 km^2 of land, around 1,500,000 km^2 have water shortages, making up the so-called "polygon of droughts" (DANTAS et al., 2002). This situation mainly affects semi-arid and arid regions, totalling around 40% of the earth's surface, and is mainly caused by factors such as climate, soil and agricultural management conditions. In this environment, plants are often exposed to various abiotic stresses such as drought, salinity and extreme temperatures (EPSTEIN et al., 1980; YANCEY et al., 1982; MAIA, 2004).

The Catolé do Rocha micro-region comprises 11 towns located in the sertão region of Paraíba, within the polygon of droughts, with caatinga as the predominant vegetation. This micro-region covers 3,038 Km^2 , with 116,056 inhabitants and a population density of 38.2 inhabitants/Km^2 . The towns that make up this micro-region have great productive potential, especially in the livestock and beekeeping sectors. According to IBGE (2010), this micro-region has a total herd of around 270,000 head of cattle, pigs, goats, sheep and poultry. In addition, in 2010, the micro-region produced more than 125 tonnes of honey, corresponding to around 47% of the total honey produced in the state of Paraíba. The region also has great agricultural potential, with a significant proportion of the population located in rural areas, carrying out family farming activities (IBGE, 2010).

We can therefore see that this scenario is ideal for implementing actions that can increase the income and development of the population of this micro-region. To this end, various state and federal projects can be implemented in the region. In particular, the Federal Government has been encouraging activities in the political, social, academic and scientific spheres that promote the development of poorer regions of the country with the aim of providing development, employment and income for rural people. One of these programmes is the PNPB (National Programme for the Production and Use of Biodiesel), which since 2004 has made important progress in

4

terms of social inclusion, job creation and income distribution among family farmers, producers of raw materials for oil production, destined for the biofuel industry (SAF/MDA, 2010). In this programme, family farmers have the essential role of supplying seeds, grains and seedlings of oilseeds, as well as extracting the oil and separating it from the bran in an integrated and sustainable agricultural system (SAF/MDA, 2010).

In relation to the PNPB, Paraíba represents only 14% of the oilseed-producing municipalities in the north-east of Brazil (SAF/MDA, 2010). Furthermore, in the state of Paraíba, these municipalities are only located in the Mata and Borborema mesoregions (SAF/MDA, 2010). It is therefore clear that the Catolé do Rocha micro-region, located in the Sertão Paraibano, has an ideal profile for the implementation of public policies for inclusion in the PNPB-Brazil. Considering the potential for livestock and honey production in the Catolé do Rocha micro-region, as well as the region's ideal profile for joining the PNPB, the demand for agricultural crops that could be used to produce animal feed, honey and oil was realised. In this context, it is understood that one of the species that meets this demand will be sunflower (*Helianthus annuus* L.).

The sunflower plant has a relatively short vegetative cycle ranging from 90 to 150 days; the crop is little influenced by latitude, longitude and photoperiod; the temperature ranges tolerated by the sunflower are around 10 to 34°C; water requirements vary from 200 mm to 900 mm per cycle, with 200 mm well distributed up to 70 days after sowing being sufficient to obtain good productivity (SENTELHAS and UNGARO, 1998; TYAGI et al, 2000; KARAM et al., 2007; LIRA et al., 2011).

Medium-textured, deep soils with good drainage, reasonable fertility and a pH varying from acidic to neutral (greater than pH 5.2) are recommended for planting sunflower (LIRA et al., 2011). The sunflower's high efficiency in exploiting the water available in the soil for its development and its tolerance to a wide temperature range mean that it is capable of producing a large amount of dry matter under conditions of water stress, without a significant reduction in production (CASTRO and FARIA, 2005). The sunflower is also considered a green fertiliser because its root system is

5

pivotal and, when left after harvest, it promotes considerable recycling of nutrients and an increase in the soil's organic matter (CASTRO et al., 1996).

The kernels have a low fibre content, but are rich in oil and protein. Around 400 kg of oil, 250 kg of husk and 350 kg of cake with 45% to 50% crude protein can be extracted from the kernels per tonne of kernels (LIRA et al., 2011). The cake, together with the vegetable matter produced, can be used as a source of fibre and protein for animal feed.

The oil produced is of excellent quality, suitable for industrial and human use (food and pharmaceuticals), its main use being as an edible oil. In addition, the cake produced as a by-product of oil extraction is an excellent animal feed; associations between sunflower cultivation and beekeeping increase both the production of honey and the oil itself due to the pollinating action of a greater number of flowers, as well as enabling complete fertilisation of the same, i.e. associated with the production of achenes, the production of honey can be a source of income, as it can produce between 30 and 40 kg of honey per hectare (MELO, 2012); the oil has also been gaining ground in the biofuel market due to its excellent chemical quality (CASTRO et al., 1996; LIRA et al., 2011).

In the global context, sunflower oil production has been in fourth place for a number of years. However, Brazil is still an insignificant producer of sunflower oil, having accounted for approximately 0.5% of world production in recent years (FAGUNDES, 2002). According to CONAB (National Supply Campaign), in 2010, the Northeast of Brazil stood out as a producing region, contributing 2% of the total planted in the country, with only the states of Rio Grande do Norte and Ceará standing out.

However, the introduction of sunflower in deforested and degraded areas of the semi-arid region for biodiesel production represents an environmental gain for these regions. Rotation with food crops also favours the preservation of the environment, since by using these areas, which were previously not being used, there will be no need to deforest new areas in order to supply the population with food (CAMARA, 2007). According to Beltrão (2007), Brazil can produce more than 60%

6

of the world's demand for renewable energy to replace oil and its derivatives, especially mineral diesel, which in the country alone consumes around 40 billion litres a year, six billion of which in agriculture. Brazil has many areas available for agriculture, without necessarily having to deforest. With the help of techniques from the various areas of agricultural engineering, there is the possibility of transforming abandoned and degraded areas into productive areas. This is one of the great challenges for expanding Brazil's agricultural frontiers and benefiting the poorest regions.

In this scenario, the polygon of droughts stands out as a region commonly affected by an irregular rainfall regime due to its insufficiency and poor distribution throughout the year. These characteristics are limiting factors for urban, industrial and agricultural development, significantly jeopardising crop yields and making it difficult to install efficient water storage systems (SANTOS JÚNIOR et al., 2011).

For plants, the abiotic stresses common to the region in question, such as water scarcity, excessive accumulation of salts in the top layers of the soil, as well as high temperatures, can drastically interfere with the growth and productivity of the crop (BOYER, 1982; EPSTEIN et al., 1980; YANCEY et al., 1982). Although the Northeast region is favourable for sunflower cultivation because it is sunny, this region has areas where crop productivity can be significantly reduced, compromising the production chain. Therefore, in order to expand sunflower-growing areas in the Northeast, water and soil management programmes, as well as programmes to obtain and characterise more drought-resistant varieties, can be implemented. It is therefore strategic to identify sunflower varieties that are adapted to and resistant to drought. Studies of this nature can also identify parameters that can be used as efficient markers to identify other genotypes.

This proposal is a continuation of the previous proposal to select promising genotypes for cultivation in the Catolé do Rocha region. At this stage, the physiological aspects involved in sunflower resistance to drought will be studied, as well as identifying genotypes that are more resistant to water deprivation stress. The project is based on the principle of training human resources at undergraduate level (PIBIC) in the areas of development and innovation in the sunflower production chain over an

7

initial period of 12 months with a grant and a bench fee. It is hoped that the results obtained in this research proposal will contribute to the inclusion of this crop as a component of rural business in Paraíba, meeting the production demands of animal feed, honey and oil in the hinterland of Paraíba, in economic systems of production chains in family farming. The aim is also to identify efficient phenological markers for the early diagnosis of genotypes that are more adapted to the dry environment. Considering that the literature is scarce in relation to this type of characterisation in sunflower grown in an irrigated system in a caatinga climate, this project is promising in terms of identifying commercially relevant resistance factors within the existing material.

1.2. OBJECTIVES

1.2.1. GENERAL OBJECTIVE

This work aims to study the relationship between morphological and phenological characters observed at early physiological stages of the plant life cycle and oil productivity in sunflower plants (*Helianthus annuus* L.) subjected to simulated drought conditions. It will also be possible to identify some biological markers associated with the early evaluation of sunflower for planting in arid environments, providing useful plant matrices for agricultural systems in regional family farming chains.

1.2.2. SPECIFIC OBJECTIVES

• To identify sunflower genotypes that are adaptable to planting in the semi-arid regions of north-eastern Brazil;

• To identify sunflower genotypes with the potential to produce grain, oil, cake and dry vegetable matter in semi-arid regions of north-eastern Brazil;

• To evaluate the effect of the growing environment in the field on the development of sunflower genotypes;

8

- Evaluate the water depth limits for sowing sunflower;

- Evaluate the limiting water depths for sunflower cultivation in the early vegetative stages of the life cycle;

- Evaluate the threshold time of resistance to irrigation restriction for sunflower cultivation in the early vegetative stages of the life cycle;

- To study the relationship between the composition of the growing substrate and the vegetative development of sunflower exposed to induced drought.

1.3. METHODOLOGY REALISED

Experiment I: Selection of sunflower genotypes adapted to growing in a semi-arid environment

This experiment was conducted in the experimental field of the Department of Agrarian and Exact Sciences at the State University of Paraíba. Between 30 and 60 days before setting up the experiments, soil and water analyses were carried out to establish the fertilisation and irrigation strategies. The nutritional and irrigation recommendations for sunflower, established in the state of Rio Grande do Norte (Lira et al., 2009) and from previous crops grown on the campus itself, were used as a reference.

For this experiment, sunflower seeds (*Helianthus annuus* L.) provided by the Agricultural Research Company of Rio Grande do Norte, Embrapa Cotton and/or national agro-industries were sown directly into the soil in shallow holes, with four to six seeds per hole. Seven days after emergence, the seedlings in the experimental stand were standardised by thinning, keeping only one plant per hole. The genotypes were grown in plots (each plot representing one genotype) with a 1.5 metre corridor between them. Each plot consisted of 4 (four) rows 1.8 m long, spaced 0.80 m apart, with only the centre rows of each plot being considered useful. All the plants in the central rows were taken into account for the phenological analyses. The distance between plants was 0.30 m in the row, totalling 6 pits/row where 03 (three) seedlings per pit would be grown and thinned out 10 (ten) days after being transferred to the field. The total and useful area of the research corresponded to approximately 4.32 m^2 , per genotype planted.

The soil was prepared by ploughing and harrowing, followed by furrowing in rows to a depth of 0.25 m, where foundation fertiliser was applied at planting and top dressing after 30 days, according to soil analysis and nutritional recommendations for the crop. Weed control was carried out manually with a brush cutter on the plots and between the beds so as not to completely cover the soil.

In order to reproduce a cultivation system without the aid of an irrigation system, the daily water table for sunflower cultivation was supplied according to the daily rainfall, which was monitored through Class A tank evaporation readings. The crop was also monitored on a daily basis and, if any pests or diseases appeared, locally-made natural pesticides were administered, depending on the disease.

Some agronomic characteristics were taken into account for the phenological assessment of the genotypes. The date of initial flowering (DFI), considered to be the period when 50% of the plants in the plot have yellow petals (Stage R4 - characterised by the first ligulate flowers, which are often yellow in colour). The date of full bloom (DFP), considered to be the period when at least 50 per cent of the flowers in the chapter are open. And the date of physiological ripeness (DMF), which was considered to be when 90% of the plants in the plot had bracts coloured between yellow and brown (30% moisture in the achenes).

Plant height was obtained by taking the average of 10 competitive plants in the useful area, measured from ground level to the insertion of the capitulum. Stem diameter was taken as the diameter of the base of the stem on the same set of plants. Leaf area was defined according to the equation AF=$0.5961(CxL)^{1,0322}$ where C=leaf length and L=leaf width, according to Maldaner et al. (2009). The number of leaves was also taken by counting all the useful leaves on the plant. All this data was taken at 30, 45 and 60 days after sowing.

At harvest time, the final stand (STDF) was also taken, obtained from the number of competitive plants in the useful area and the fresh mass values of the aerial part and root, as well as the number of achenes and the dry weight of the grains.of the

10

chapter.

The experimental design was a randomised block with 4 replicates and all the data was submitted to statistical analysis to test for significance and differences in means at the 5% confidence level.

In this experiment, at least two of the most productive genotypes were selected to be used in subsequent experiments.

Experiment II: Evaluation of the level of sunflower resistance to drought induced at the germination stage

The genotypes to be used were those defined in experiment I. Sunflower seeds were sown in plastic germination trays in a washed sand substrate and dried in an oven.

The seeds of the genotypes were previously selected and then sown in 200-cell Gerbox® trays, using washed, dried and sieved sand as a substrate. The experiment was carried out in a greenhouse under the region's environmental conditions (12h light photoperiod, 28±4°C, 15% relative humidity). The genotypes were irrigated at 10, 20, 30, 40, 50, 60 and 70 per cent of field capacity, with the 70 per cent treatment considered the control. The trays were weighed daily to determine the level of water to be applied to each treatment. Phenological analyses were carried out throughout the experimental period. 10 days after sowing, the seedlings were collected, separated into aerial parts and roots and further analyses were carried out.

The experimental design will be entirely causal with a 2 x 7 factorial (genotypes, water depth, respectively) using five replicates. Significant differences will be determined using the F test and the means will be compared using the Tukey test at a 5% confidence level.

The following parameters were evaluated for this experiment:

a) Germination speed index, obtained from the formula: $IVG = (N1G1+N2G2+...+NnGn)/ (G1+G2+...+Gn)$ Where: $G1, G2,...Gn$ is the number of seeds germinated on the day of observation; $N1, N2,..., Nn$ is the number of days of observation, according to Edmond and Drapalla (1958);

11

b) Germination percentage, calculated using the formula: $G = (\Sigma ni \cdot N\text{-}1)$. 100 Where: Σni is the total number of seeds germinated in relation to the number of seeds placed to germinate (Borghetti and Ferreira, 2004);

c) Length of aerial and root parts, taken with the aid of a ruler;

d) Fresh and dry mass of the aerial and root parts, taken using a scale, where the dry mass was obtained after drying in an oven at 70° C for 72 hours.

Experiment III: Evaluation of the level of sunflower resistance to drought induced in the crop's slow vegetative growth stage

The genotypes to be used were those defined in experiment I. Sunflower seeds were sown in plastic seedling bags filled with the same soil used in experiment I. The seeds of the genotypes were previously selected and then sown four per plastic bag. The experiment was conducted in a seedling nursery under the environmental conditions of the region (12h light photoperiod, 28±4°C, 15% relative humidity). All the plants were irrigated at 70 per cent of field capacity. 30 days after sowing, the genotypes will be irrigated at 10, 20, 30, 40, 50, 60 and 70 per cent of field capacity, considering the 70 per cent treatment as the control. Soil moisture will be determined daily to control the water supplied in the irrigation of each treatment. Phenological analyses were carried out throughout the experimental period. Collections were made according to the appearance of damage caused by the treatments. Samples were collected, separated into aerial parts and roots and further analyses were carried out.

The experimental design will be entirely randomised with a 2 x 7 factorial (genotypes, water depth, respectively) using five replicates. Significant differences in the parameters assessed will be determined using the F test and the means will be compared using the Tukey test at a 5% confidence level.

The following parameters will be assessed for this experiment:

a) Number of leaves per plant;

b) Leaf damage index per plant: taken from an arbitrary numerical scale from 1 to 5, which will be related to the visual appearance of leaf damage, assessed daily.

c) Diameter of the stem, taken using a caliper;

d) Height of the aerial part, taken with the aid of a ruler.

1.4. RESULTS

Experiment I: Selection of sunflower genotypes adapted to growing in a semi-arid environment

Sunflower genotypes were analysed in terms of biomass production throughout vegetative development, as well as biomass and final grain yield after harvest. Development analyses were carried out at 30, 45 and 60 days after sowing (DAS), analysing plant height, stem diameter, number of leaves and total leaf area (Figure 1). In these terms, it was possible to define that vegetative development was most intense between the 30th and 45th days after sowing. And 45th. DAS. In addition, in the four variables observed, there was no difference between the 45th and 60th DAS measurements. DAS, indicating that there was no apparent vegetative growth during this period, except for the height of the BRSG01, HELIO253 and HELIO250 genotypes.

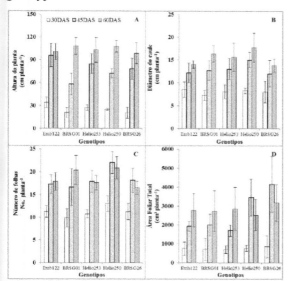

Figure 1. Plant height (A); stem diameter (B); number of leaves (C) and; total leaf area (D) of five sunflower genotypes grown in a semi-arid environment, observed at 30, 45 and 60 days after sowing.

13

Aspects of the genotypes' reproductive development were also checked throughout development, analysing the date of initial and full flowering, as well as the date of physiological maturity (Table 1). The dates of initial and full flowering and the date of physiological ripeness were also defined. With regard to early flowering, the EMB122 and Helio253 genotypes stood out as the earliest and the BRSG01 and BRSG26 genotypes as the latest. With regard to full flowering, Helio253 was considered the earliest, while BRSG26 was considered the latest. However, the EMB122 and Helio250 genotypes stood out for being the earliest and latest (respectively) in terms of maturity.

Table 1. Date of initial flowering, Date of full flowering and Date of physiological maturity of sunflower genotypes grown in the field, counting from the day of sowing.

Genotypes	Initial Flowering	Full bloom	Physiological Maturation
Emb122	49	55	75
BRSG01	55	63	82
Helio253	49	53	78
Helio250	54	58	85
BRSG26	55	64	77

After harvesting, the Fresh Mass (MF) of the aerial part and root was obtained (Figure 2). Proportionally, all the genotypes accumulated more mass and water in the aerial part than in the roots, with the BRSG01 and Helio250 genotypes accumulating the most MF, while the Emb122 and BRSG26 genotypes accumulated the least MF in the aerial part of the plants. On the other hand, the BRSG01 genotype accumulated more MF in the roots, with no apparent differences between the two genotypes.

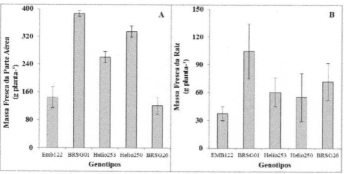

Figure 2: Fresh mass of aerial part (A) and roots (B) of five sunflower genotypes grown in a semi-arid environment.

Productivity was also assessed in relation to the number of achenes produced per plant and the dry mass of these achenes (Figure 3). The most productive genotype was Helio253, while BRSG26 was the least productive. However, there were no

14

differences in the dry matter content of the achenes.

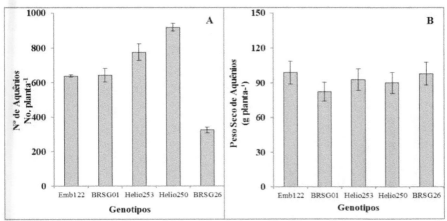

Figure 3: Number of achenes (A) and dry weight of achenes (B) of five sunflower genotypes grown in a semi-arid environment.

On the basis of this experiment, with regard to biomass and achene production and their origin, in an attempt to compare a hybrid with a cultivar, the BRSG01 and Helio253 genotypes were defined as the most impactful for cultivation in the semi-arid environment. These genotypes will be considered as models for subsequent experiments.

Experiment II: Evaluation of the level of sunflower resistance to drought induced at the germination stage

Seeds of two sunflower genotypes were germinated over 10 days in different soil moisture conditions, kept at 70 - control, 60, 50, 40, 30, 20 and 10 per cent of the substrate's field capacity, and were assessed in terms of the number of germinated plants, germination percentage, aerial and root length, fresh mass (MF) and dry mass (MS) of aerial and root parts. Over the 10 days there was an average germination efficiency of 90 per cent for both genotypes, except for those treated with 10 per cent of field capacity (Figure 4). Helio253 seeds treated with 20% of field capacity also suffered from the reduction in the amount of water, with a germination efficiency of around 50% (Figure 4). In general, the time needed for the seeds to germinate was between 2 and 7 days, depending on the amount of water in the substrate, where the time needed for germination was inversely proportional to the amount of water in the substrate (Figure 5). However, the Helio253 genotype germinated more slowly and with greater homogeneity than the BRSG01 genotype (Figure 5).

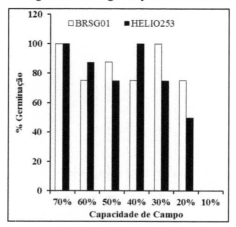

Figura 4. % total germination of the experimental stand total germination of sunflower genotypes BRSG01 (A) and HELIO253 (B), 10 days after sowing, subjected to water restriction treatments (70 - control; 60; 50; 40; 30; 20 and 10% of field capacity.

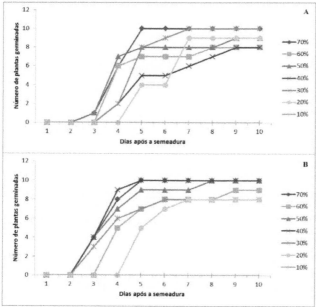

Figura 5. Germination rate of sunflower genotypes BRSG01 (A) and HELIO253 (B) observed over 10 days

16

and subjected to water restriction treatments (70 - control; 60; 50; 40; 30; 20 and 10% of field capacity.

The length of the aerial part was reduced proportionally to the reduction in the amount of water in the substrate, with the BRSG01 genotype suffering a sharper reduction proportional to the reduction in the amount of water (Figure 6A). It appears that the treatment with 60% of field capacity increased the length of the aerial part of BRSG01 by 20%, while the 20% dose, the minimum acceptable, decreased the aerial part of this genotype by up to 65% (Figure 6A). The development of the root system was also affected (Figure 6B). From the 50% dose onwards, there was an increase of around 10% in the root length of both genotypes. At the 60% dose, while BRSG01 suffered no effect from the treatment, the Helio253 genotype had a root about 50% longer than its respective control (Figure 6B).

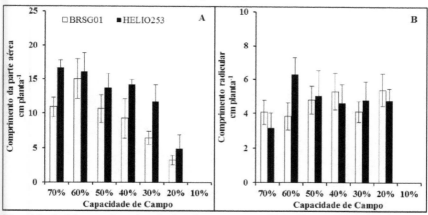

Figura 6. Aerial part and root length of sunflower genotypes BRSG01 (A) and HELIO253 (B), 10 days after sowing, subjected to water restriction treatments (70 - control; 60; 50; 40; 30; 20 and 10% of field capacity.

When analysing the fresh and dry mass content of the aerial parts and roots, it was observed that for the BRSG01 genotype there was a drastic reduction in the MF content of the tissues, much greater than in the Helio253 genotype (Figure 7A). This variation was not reflected in the DM, indicating that the reduction in mass was caused by the loss of water from the tissues (Figure 7B). However, it is clear that BRSG01 seedlings accumulate more green mass in the aerial part than the Helio253 genotype at this stage of vegetative development. When analysing roots, it was possible to see that there were no drastic changes in the MF and DM of both genotypes, except at the 30%

17

dose (Figure 7C and D).

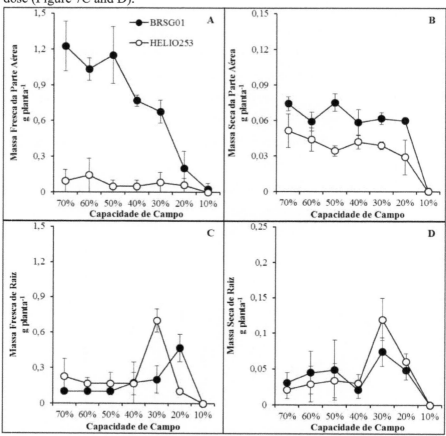

Figure 7 - Fresh mass (A and C) and dry mass (B and D) of aerial parts (A and B) and roots (C and D) of sunflower genotypes BRSG01 (A) and HELIO253 (B), 10 days after sowing, subjected to water restriction treatments (70 - control; 60; 50; 40; 30; 20 and 10% of field capacity).

In this context, it was possible to verify that the Helio253 genotype suffered less influence from the water restriction treatments than the BRSG01 genotype. Furthermore, the minimum possible dose to enable sunflower germination is 20% of the substrate's water retention capacity and up to a dose of 40% it is possible to have efficient germination without widespread damage to the Helio253 genotype, as shown by the germination rate, germination %, length, fresh and dry matter of the aerial part and root.

Experiment III: Evaluation of the level of sunflower resistance to drought induced in the crop's slow vegetative growth stage

Sunflower plants of the BRSG01 and Helio253 genotypes were subjected to treatments with 70 - control, 60, 50, 40, 30, 20 and 10% of field capacity, from 30 days after sowing, taking into account the number of leaves, injury index, stem diameter and shoot height. The number of leaves was visibly affected in both genotypes (Figure 8). In general, within four days of observation, the 70 per cent dose led to an increase in the number of leaves in both genotypes. However, the 60 and 50% doses paralysed the production of new leaves and from these doses onwards, throughout the observation period, the plants lost viable leaves.

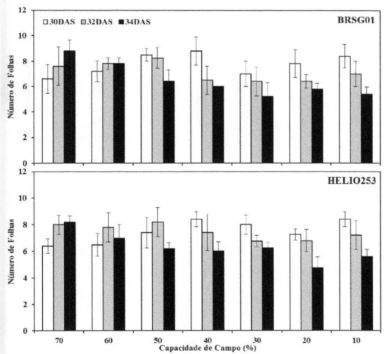

Figure 8. Number of leaves of sunflower genotypes BRS01 and HELIO253 subjected to water restriction treatments by regulating field capacity. Plants observed at 30, 32 and 34 days after sowing.

The effect of the doses was best visualised by analysing the aerial damage index. 30 days after sowing, the maximum damage was seen on the first day of observation, starting with the treatment at 20% of field capacity (Figure 9).

19

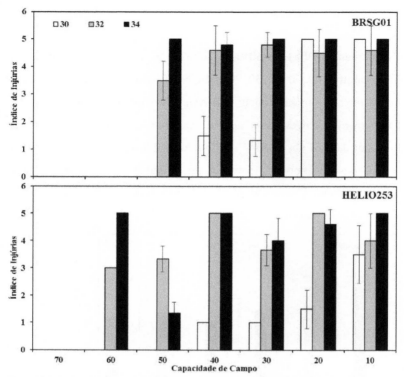

Figure 9. Injury index of sunflower genotypes BRS01 and HELIO253 subjected to water restriction treatments by regulating field capacity. Plants observed at 30, 32 and 34 days after sowing.

With regard to stem diameter, observing the development over the four days of observation, the BRSG01 genotype maintained the increase only until the 60 per cent treatment (Figure 10). The Hélio253 genotype, on the other hand, apparently maintained stem development until the 30% treatment (Figure 10).

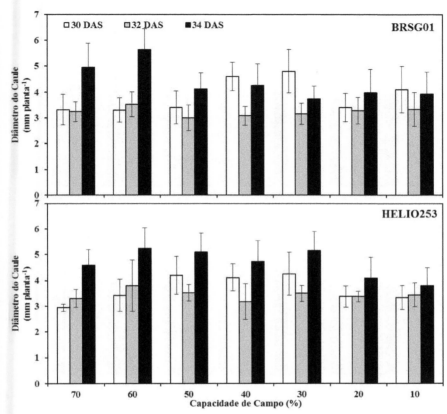

Figure 10. Stem diameter of sunflower genotypes BRS01 and HELIO253 subjected to water restriction treatments by regulating field capacity. Plants observed at 30, 32 and 34 days after sowing.

With regard to shoot height, there were no apparent changes in plant height in all treatments and in both genotypes (Figure 11).

21

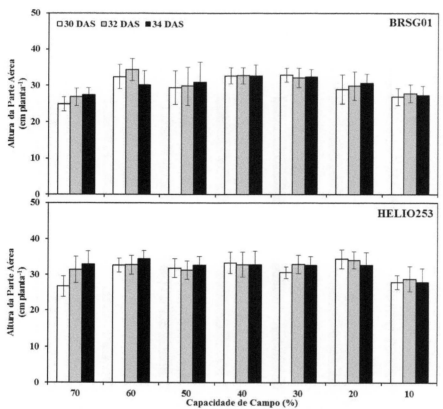

Figure 11. Aerial part height of sunflower genotypes BRS01 and HELIO253 subjected to water restriction treatments by regulating field capacity. Plants observed at 30, 32 and 34 days after sowing.

From the evidence gathered, it can be concluded that both genotypes suffered the effects of the treatment. More broadly, the effects are most evident in the form of visual damage. However, they can still be relatively easily detected by analysing the diameter of the stem and the number of leaves. Considering the injury index as a strong indicator of damage, it is suggested that treatment at 20 per cent of field capacity is borderline and that below this the species suffers irreparable damage.

1.5. FINAL CONSIDERATIONS

In view of the above, the genotypes best suited to growing in semi-arid environments are BRSG01 and Helio253. These genotypes are capable of germinating at up to 20 per cent of field capacity in water in the substrate and can possibly maintain

22

their vegetative development at up to 40 per cent of field capacity. Further studies should be carried out to find explanations for this level of resistance.

1.6. BIBLIOGRAPHICAL REFERENCES

BELTRÃO, N. E. de M.; OLIVEIRA, M. I. P. de. **Potential oilseeds in the Northeast for biodiesel production**. Campina Grande - PB, ISSN 0103-0205, 2007.

BORGHETTI, F.; FERREIRA, A. G. Interpretation of germination results. In: FERREIRA, A. G.; BORGHETTI, F. (Org.). **Germination - from basic to applied**. Porto Alegre: Artmed, 2004.

BOYER, J. S. **Plant productivity and environment.** Science, v. 218, p. 443-448, 1982.

CAMARA, R. **Sunflower is one of the main oilseeds for biodiesel in the semi-arid region** (2007). Available at: http://www.correiodatarde.com.br/ editorias/correio_ambiental-20750. Accessed on: 03 March 2012.

CASTRO, C.; FARIAS, J.R.B. **Sunflower ecophysiology.** In: LEITE, E.M.V.B. de C. BRIGHENTI, A.M.; CASTRO, C. de (Ed.). Sunflower in Brazil. Londrina: Embrapa Soja, p. 163-218. 2005.

CASTRO,C.; CASTIGLIONI, V.B.R.; BALLA, A. **The sunflower crop: production technology**. Documentos, EMBRAPA-CNPSo, Londrina n. 67, 20p.,1996.

DANTAS, J. P.; MARINHO, F. J. L.; FERREIRA, M. M. M.; AMORIM, M. do S. N.; ANDRADE, S. I. de O.; SALES, A. L. de. **Evaluation of string bean genotypes under salinity.** Revista Brasileira de Engenharia Agrícola e Ambiental, v. 6, n. 3, p.425-430, 2002.

EDMOND, J.B.; DRAPALLA, W.J. The effects of temperature, sand and soil, and acetone on germination on okra seeds. **Proceedings of the American Society Horticultural Science**, v.71, p.428-434, 1958.

EPSTEIN, E.; NORLYN, J. D.; RUSH, D.W.; KINGSBURY, R. W.; KELLY, D. B.; CUNNINGHAM, G. A.; WRONA, A. F. **Saline culture of crops: a genetic approach,** Science, v. 210, p.399-404, 1980.

IBGE - Brazilian Institute of Geography and Statistics. **Cidades@, 2010 data.** Available at: http://www.ibge.gov.br/cidadesat/painel/painel.php?codmun= 250430#, Accessed on: 14/07/2012.

KARAM, D.; MAGALHÃES, P.C.; PADILHA, L. **Effect of the addition of polymers on the viability, vigour and longevity of maize seeds.** Sete Lagoas: Embrapa Milho e Sorgo, 2007. 5p (Embrapa milho e Sorgo. Circular Técnica, 94) http://www.cnpms.embrapa.br/publicacoes/publica/2007/circular/Circ_94.pdf, Accessed on: 05 Feb. 2009.

LIRA, M.A.; CARVALHO, H.W.L. de; CHAGAS, M.C.M. das; BRISTOT, G.; DANTAS, J.A.;LIMA, J.M.P. de. **Evaluation of the potential of sunflower as an alternative crop in the semi-arid northeast.** Natal: ENPARN, 2011. Documentos, n. 40, 43p.

LIRA, M.A.; CHAGAS, M.C.M.; BRISTOT, G.; DANTAS, J.A.; HOLANDA, J.S.; LIMA, J.M.P. **Recomendações Técnicas para o Cultivo do Girassol.** Natal: EMPARN, 2009.

MAIA, J. M. Additive and interactive effect of drought and NaCl treatments on the antioxidative response of cowpea roots [Vigna unguiculata L.(Walp.)].

(Master's dissertation). Department of Biochemistry and Molecular Biology, Federal University of Ceara, Fortaleza, CE, 2004, 126p.

MELO, Y. L. de. Characterisation and agronomic performance of sunflower genotypes (*Helianthus annuus* L.) in terms of phenological, physiological and biochemical markers in different edaphoclimatic micro-regions of Rio Grande do Norte. (**Master's thesis**) Department of Plant Science. Federal Rural University of the Semi-Arid. 2012.

SAF/MDA - Secretariat of Family Agriculture/Ministry of Agrarian Development. **National Programme for the Production and Use of Biodiesel** (2010). Available at: http://www.google.com.br/url?sa=t&rct=j&q=&esrc=s&source=web&cd=2&ved=0C FEQFjAB&url=http%3A%2F%2Fwww.mda.gov.br%2Fportal%2Fsaf%2Farquivos% 2Fview%2Fnsmail.pdf&ei=Fq8BUM_yN4aF0QHarKDgBw&usg=AFQjCNEz2F8u2 _lkttN2A55sYeD6ureA2A, Accessed on: 14/07/2012

SANTOS JÚNIOR, J.A.; GHEYI, H.R.; DIAS, N. da S.; SOARES, F.A.L.;NOBRE, R.G. **Doses of boron and wastewater in sunflower production.** Revista Ciência Agronômica, v.42, n.4, p.857-864, 2011.

SENTELHAS, P. C.; UNGARO, M.R.G. **Bioclimatic indices for sunflower cultivation.** Scientia Agrícola, Piracicaba, v.55, n.1. p.1-10, 1998.

TYAGI, S.; MARRA, S.A.E, KRAMER, F.R. Wavelength-shifting molecular beacons. **Natural biotechnology**, 2000; 18-11910/6.

YANCEY, P. H.; CLARK, M. E.; HAND S. C.; BOWLUS, R.D.; SOMERO, G. N. Living with water stress: evolution of osmolyte sustems, **Science**, v. 217, p 12141222, 1982.

CHAPTER 2

Grafted cashew seedlings subjected to saline conditions

SUMMARY

Abiotic stress factors are responsible for the loss of agricultural production worldwide, especially in semi-arid regions where adverse conditions such as high temperatures associated with drought, salinity and excessive solar radiation prevail. These factors, alone or in combination, cause intense disturbances in plant metabolism. Salinity causes an intense reduction in photosynthetic capacity, which is associated with the induction of cellular oxidative damage. In this context, we set out to elucidate the physiological mechanisms involved in the resistance of grafts and rootstocks used to obtain grafted cashew seedlings exposed to salinity. For this work, the intensity of the stress caused by salinity was analysed based on measurements of leaf area, number of leaves, plant height, dry mass, Na content$^+$, K$^+$ and Ca^{+2} , percentage of humidity, relative leaf water content and percentage of membrane damage in grafted cashew seedlings subjected to three increasing doses of NaCl. The experiment was carried out in a completely randomised design with treatments arranged in a 4 x 3 factorial, four combinations of grafted seedlings (CCP 09/CCP 09, CCP 09/CCP 76/CCP 76, CCP 76/CCP 09) and three doses of NaCl (0-control, 50 and 100 mM), for 30 days. There were five replicates per treatment, totalling 60 plots, each represented by a pot containing a seedling. Based on the data analysed, it is clear that early dwarf cashew seedlings subjected to salt treatments with 50 and 100 mM NaCl showed obvious damage, as well as different response patterns in relation to the parameters analysed. It is possible to see differences between the seedlings by analysing the percentage of leaf moisture, relative leaf water content, percentage of leaf dry mass, leaf area, number of leaves and content of Na ions$^+$, K$^+$ and Ca^{+2} . In addition, according to the variables analysed, the CCP09/CCP76 seedlings and especially CCP76/CCP09 were less affected by the salt treatments than the other seedling combinations.

Keywords: Grafts, Salinity, *Anacardium occidentale*.

2.1. INTRODUCTION

Cashew cultivation is one of the most important agricultural activities in the Northeast of Brazil, both socially (large number of jobs) and economically through the export of nuts (Ferreira-Silva et al., 2009). According to the Federation of Industry and Commerce of the State of Ceará (FIEC, 2012), in 2012 Ceará traded 160.1 million dollars worth of chestnuts, representing 13.6% of total exports. This performance, however, is 16 per cent lower than in 2011, when 190.5 million dollars were sold. In all cases, the productivity of this crop is extremely low when compared to its production potential. According to FIEC (2012), the installed processing capacity of the Ceará industry is approximately 300,000 tonnes per year, but it is currently working with less than 100,000 tonnes per year. In the Northeast as a whole, there are 600,000 tonnes that could be processed, and this potential is not being well exploited.

With a view to improving plantations, the governments of northeastern states such as Paraíba, Rio Grande do Norte and Ceará are always investing in improving cashew farming, including family farming. For example, in 2012, the state government of Paraíba invested 49 million dollars in agriculture with resources from the International Fund for Agricultural Development, including cashew farming among other activities (Paraíba, 2012). In Rio Grande do Norte, an investment programme in cashew farming was launched in 2012 with support from the Banco do Nordeste, with the aim of increasing productivity in the Oeste Potiguar region (Emater, 2011). In 2000, another important programme in the state of Ceará boosted productivity by replacing canopies on unproductive cashew trees with the introduction of early dwarf cashew clones (Barros et al., 2000). These three states together account for around 30 per cent of Brazil's nut production (IBGE, 2011). However, the use of inferior quality seedlings causes economic losses due to the lack of utilisation of the region's full production potential.

Another problem that influences productivity is the cashew tree's narrow genetic base (Barros et al, 2000), which makes it vulnerable and can jeopardise its expansion, especially to marginal areas subject to environmental stress. In addition, the main method of vegetative propagation (grafting) uses an extremely small number of materials as rootstocks for the most productive clones. It is known in other crops, particularly *Citrus,* that the type of rootstock has a strong influence on the quality of the seedling, especially under stress conditions (Banuls and Primo-Milo, 1995). In fact, one method of reducing production losses is grafting, as this strategy can provide a means of combining the salinity resistance characteristics of the rootstock with the best fruit quality and high productivity of the aerial part (scion), resulting in more productive grafted plants under saline conditions (Estan et al. 2005).

27

Unfortunately, in the case of cashew, there is very little research into the genetic variability of the current materials available, especially for environmental stress conditions such as salinity (Ponte et al., 2011). In Brazil, the initial work to improve the early dwarf cashew tree consisted of individual phenotypic selection, followed by annual production control on the selected plants. This work began in 1965 at the Pacajus-CE Experimental Station. This methodology, although simple and with low genetic gains, led to the commercial launch of the current clones CCP 06 and CCP 76 in 1983, CCP 09 and CCP 1001 in 1987 and, more recently, EMBRAPA clones 50 and 51 (Almeida et al, 1992). The existence of few commercial dwarf cashew clones recommended for commercial planting in the region, coupled with the excessively narrow genetic base from which these clones originated (Almeida et al, 1992; Barros et al., 1993), clearly characterises a situation of genetic vulnerability. Therefore, the selection of rootstocks that are more tolerant to salinity represents an important step towards the expansion and sustainability of cashew cultivation. However, tolerance to abiotic stresses is a quantitative characteristic that involves the expression of several genes (Bohnert and Jensen, 1996). In turn, knowledge of the most important physiological characters in tolerance is essential for selection and genetic improvement programmes.

The expression of biochemical and physiological traits linked to salt stress tolerance involves genetic and environmental factors. In the case of grafted seedlings, it is important to define which characteristics are transferred by each plant part involved. One of the strategies used to select more tolerant rootstocks, as in the case of tomatoes, is to use wild materials as a source of resistance (Fageria and Gheyi, 1997). In the case of cashew trees, the use of other species such as *A. microcarpum* could be an option, given that it grows spontaneously in the conditions of north-eastern Brazil (Barros, 1998). In addition, other cashew matrices developed under saline conditions, such as those found in dune areas, could serve as a source of genetic diversity for salt stress tolerance.

Therefore, one possibility for obtaining materials (grafted cashew plants) that are more resistant to salinity in terms of these metabolic processes would be to combine grafts (aerial part) with rootstocks that have a better photosynthetic capacity in saline conditions. Based on observations already made, this better performance of grafted plants can be attributed in part to resistance characteristics of both the scion and the rootstock, although the physiological mechanisms of this compatibility are still poorly understood.

2.2. OBJECTIVES

2.2.1. General Objective

Elucidate the physiological mechanisms involved in the resistance of grafts and rootstocks used to obtain grafted cashew seedlings exposed to salinity.

2.1.2. Specific Objectives

Verify the intensity of the stress caused by salinity based on measurements of leaf area, number of leaves, plant height, fresh mass, dry mass, Na content$^+$, K+ and Ca^{+2} , percentage of humidity, relative leaf water content (RWC) and percentage of membrane damage (%DM) in grafted cashew seedlings subjected to three increasing doses of NaCl.

2.3. METHODOLOGY

The work was carried out in protected cultivation at the Centre for Human and Agricultural Sciences (CCHA), Campus IV of the State University of Paraíba (UEPB), located in the municipality of Catolé do Rocha - PB, situated at 6° 1' S latitude and 37° 48' O longitude, at an altitude of 50m. The region's climate is of the BSw'h type, according to the Koppen classification, and is characterised by being hot semi-arid, with two distinct seasons, one rainy with irregular rainfall and the other with no rainfall. The average annual rainfall is 870 mm and the average temperature is 27°C.

2.3.1. Statistical design

The experiment was carried out in a completely randomised design with treatments arranged in a 4 x 3 factorial, four combinations of seedlings

grafted (CCP 09/CCP 09, CCP 09/CCP 76/CCP 76, CCP 76/CCP 09) and three doses of NaCl (0-control, 50 and 100 mM), for 30 days. There were five replicates per treatment, totalling 60 plots, each represented by a pot containing one seedling. The data relating to the variables measured were subjected to the F test at 0.05% significance, using analysis of variance, and the means of the variables were subjected to the Tukey test at the same probability level.

2.3.2. Setting up and running the experiment

To set up the experiment in the experimental field at UEPB, Campus IV, 60 plastic pots with a capacity of four litres each were used. The pots were pierced at the bottom for drainage.

The substrate was then prepared, containing a mixture of vermiculite and sand in a 1/1 ratio. The pots were then filled and the amount of substrate standardised by weighing. The pots were then placed in a protected environment (Figure 01).

Figure 01. Final stand of grafted plants in a protected environment.

2.3.3. Planting and Cultivation

Early dwarf cashew seedlings from Serra Talhada - PE, were obtained from

30

the following scion/rootstock combinations: CCP 09/CCP 09

(self grafting of CCP 09), CCP 09/ CCP 76, CCP 76/CCP 76 (self grafting of CCP 76) and CCP 76/CCP 09 according to the methodology described in Ferreira-Silva et al. (2010). The plants were transported to Catolé do Rocha in seedling bags. The plants were first acclimatised to the location for approximately 15 days. After this period they were transferred to plastic pots and kept under water irrigation for a further 15 days, where irrigation with Hoagland's % strength nutrient solution (Hoagland and Arnon, 1950) began. Fifteen days after starting irrigation with the nutrient solution, the saline treatments were implemented, including salt in the nutrient solution, following the combination of treatments.

The humidity of the substrate was kept close to field capacity (FC). During exposure to salt, vegetative growth measurements were taken on the different scion/rootstock combinations at 15 and 30 DAT (two measurements). As the experiment progressed, the necessary weeding was carried out to maintain the facilities according to the level of infestation in the experimental area, in order to make the environment free of spontaneous vegetation, offering favourable conditions for the development of the crop under study.

After the seedlings had been subjected to salinity for 15 days, data was collected to check for changes in the parameters studied between the four graftings subjected to different levels of saline solution.

2.1.1. Biometric variables

Determination of leaf area (LA) and number of leaves (NF)

During a period to be observed at an interval of 15 days, leaf width and length were measured for subsequent determination of leaf area (LA) (cm^2) using the equations: $A = 0.21 + O, 69$ L.C ($R2 = 0.97$) and $A = -44.28 + 14.32$ L ($R2 = 0.90$) (MURTHY et al.1985) where: L= leaf width; C= leaf length.

31

Flexible rulers graduated in millimetres were used for the measurements, which were placed on the leaves in the transverse and longitudinal plane to the central vein of the leaves in millimetres. The number of leaves (NF) was also evaluated by counting all the leaves on the seedlings respectively.

Plant height (AP)

Measurements were also taken of the length of the main branch, estimating plant height (PH) in cm. Flexible rulers graduated in millimetres were used to measure the length of the main branch. For the measurements, a standard position was adopted, in which the ruler was positioned flush with the ground and extending close to the plant's apical bud.

Growth by fresh mass

The different parts of the plants, roots, stems and leaves, were collected and immediately weighed on an analyser to obtain the fresh mass.

Na content$^+$, K$^+$ and Ca^{+2}

The extraction of Na$^+$, K$^+$ and Ca^{+2}) from leaf tissues was carried out using 50 mg of plant tissue in 20 mL of deionised water in a water bath at 100 °C for 1 hour, in hermetically sealed screw-top tubes. The clear extract was filtered and the sodium content was measured using a flame photometer (Malavolta et al., 1997).

Relative leaf water content (RWC) and humidity percentage (%U)

Leaf discs were collected and the fresh mass (MF) was determined on a semi-analytical balance. The parts were then incubated in deionised distilled water for 4 hours and the turgid mass (TM) was measured. Finally, the parts were dried in an oven at 70°C for 48 hours and the dry mass (DM) was determined. The relative water content (RWC) was calculated according to the relationship described by Irigoyen et al. (1992): CRA = (MF-MS/MT-MS) x 100 (%). The percentage of leaf moisture will be obtained using the following equation: %U = [(MFMS)/MF]x100.

Percentage of membrane damage (%DM)

The degree of membrane integrity was estimated by electrolyte leakage according to Lutts et al. (1996), with minor modifications. Ten 10 mm diameter leaf discs were collected and placed in test tubes with 10 mL of deionised water and incubated in a water bath at 25°C for 6 hours. Then the electrical conductivity of the solutions (L_1) was determined using a conductivity meter. The tubes were then placed back in a water bath for one hour at 100°C and new electrical conductivity readings were taken (L_2). Membrane damage, estimated by the percentage of electrolyte leakage, was calculated using the ratio: %VE = (L1/L2) x 100.

2.4. RESULTS

In this study of the respective grafted clones, the control seedlings developed normally, free of apparent damage and turgid. It can also be seen that the symptoms of damage and growth restriction caused by NaCl were visible in all graft combinations in the 50mM and 100 mM treatments after 5 days of exposure (Figure 02). At the end of the experimental period (30 days after sowing), drastic visual symptoms of leaf damage were observed, including leaf drop in clones CCP09/CCP09, CCP09/CCP76, CCP76/CCP76 and CCP76/CCP09 (Figure 02). Both the autografts of clones CCP09/CCP09 and CCP09/CCP76 stood out for showing less obvious symptoms of toxicity. Symptoms of leaf damage in the 4 graftings were evident in the oldest leaves (primary leaves) with subsequent progression to the youngest fully expanded leaves. The symptoms were characterised by the appearance of chlorosis on the leaf limb, progressing to dryness with necrosis from the margins to the centre, followed by the primary leaves falling from the treatment with the highest concentration of 100 mM

NaCl, as shown in Figure 02. It should be noted that there was significant variability in the intensity of visual symptoms within each treatment. However, height was not drastically affected in any of the rootstock combinations under any of the salt treatments applied (Figure 03), remaining between 19 and 27 cm in height

0   50   100
mmol L^{-1} NaCl

Figure 02. Morphological aspect of early dwarf cashew plants grafted onto the following scion/scion combinations: CCP09/CCCP09; CCP09/CCC76; CCP76/CCCP09; CCP76/CCP76, 30 days after the start of treatment. The plants were subjected to 0 (control), 50 and 100 mM NaCl treatments. New leaves were produced in the control and chlorosis and necrosis in the salt treatments, especially in the treatment with 100 mM NaCl.

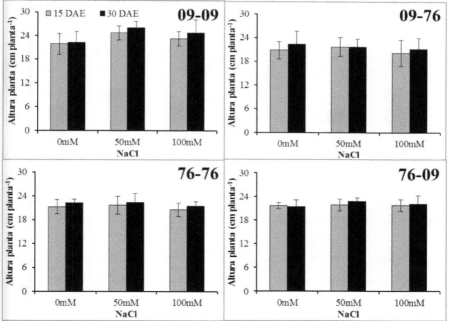

Figure 03. Height of grafted early dwarf cashew plants, subjected to 0, 50 and 100 mM NaCl treatments, observed at 15 and 30 days after the onset of stress (DAT).

Among the grafted clones exposed to high salt treatments, there was also no drastic effect on the number of leaves when analysed at 15 DAT, with the CCP76/CCP09 graft standing out, where there was an increase in the number of leaves at the 50mM dose. When the seedlings were exposed to salt stress for a longer period of time (30 DAT), the CCP09/CCP09, CCP09/CCP76 and CCP76/CCP76 grafts had a drastic reduction in the number of leaves at the 50mM and 100mM doses. This effect may be due to the long period of exposure to the salts, assimilating a large amount of toxic ions into the plant tissues causing morphophysiological damage (Figure 04).

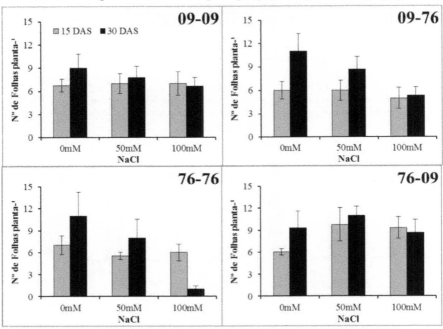

Figure 04. Number of leaves of grafted early dwarf cashew plants subjected to 0, 50 and 100 mM NaCl treatments, observed at 15 and 30 days after the onset of stress (DAE).

In relation to leaf area, it was observed that the grafts assessed after 15 DAT did not correspond significantly, with a small variation between the treatments exposed, with an increase for the CCP76/CCP09 graft at a concentration of 50 mM and a decrease in leaf area as the concentration of salinity increased. When the cashew grafts were analysed at 30 DAT, a drastic reduction in leaf area was observed in the CCP09/CCP09, CCP09/CCP76 and CCP76/CCP76 grafts. At doses of 50mM and 100mM, it was observed that the leaf area reduced proportionally to the increase in salinity. The CCP76/CCP09 scion differed from the others, reaching the greatest leaf area at the 50mM dose, possibly due to an osmotic effect, maintaining a gradient between the leaves (old and young) thus avoiding the concentration of toxic ions in the young leaves, where they are in the process of leaf expansion (Figure 05).

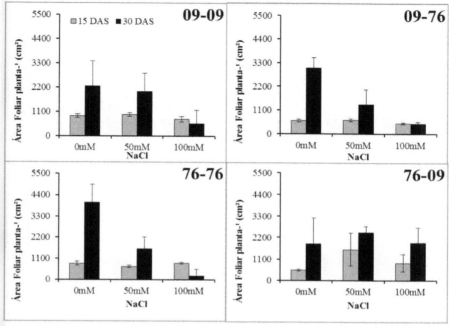

Figure 05. Leaf area of grafted early dwarf cashew plants submitted to 0, 50 and 100 mM NaCl treatments, observed at 15 and 30 days after the start of stress (DAT).

For the percentage of leaf moisture, the CCP76/CCP09 scion stood out in relation to the others, remaining practically constant throughout the increase in salt dosages. The CCP09/CCP09 scion showed a drastic decrease when treated with 100mM NaCl. There were no statistically significant variations in the percentage of moisture in the upper stem, lower stem and root. It was also observed that the percentage of moisture in the upper stem of CCP09/CCP09 plants remained stable at the highest concentrations, while the moisture of the CCP09/CCP76 scion was lower at 50mM and 100mM NaCl levels, compared to the other grafts. On the other hand, the autograft CCP09/CCP09 showed the least variation when subjected to salt stress, maintaining a lower percentage of stem moisture in all treatments when compared to the other grafts and the high graft CCP76/CCP76. In the roots, the percentage of moisture was higher in the CCP76/CCP09 scion in all treatments and in the CCP76/CCP76 self-scion there was a decrease proportional to the salt dose (Figure 06).

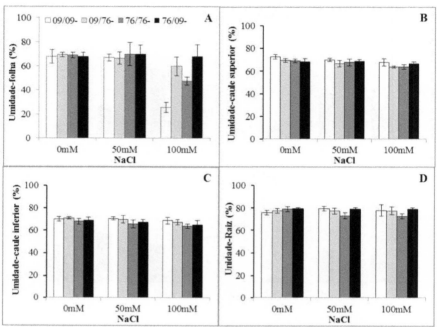

Figure 06. Moisture percentage of leaves (A), upper stem (B), lower stem (C) and roots (D) of grafted early dwarf cashew plants subjected to 0, 50 and 100 mM NaCl treatments, observed at 15 and 30 days after the onset of stress (DAE).

The percentage of leaf dry mass was practically constant from the control up to the 50mM dosage, after which there was an increase at the 100mM concentration in all the grafts, but it can be seen that the CCP09/CCP09 autograft stood out from the others, while the CCP76/CCP09 graft obtained the lowest values. The percentages of dry mass of the upper and lower stems showed a slight increase in all the grafts as the concentrations increased. As for the percentage of root dry mass, there was no insignificant effect (Figure 07).

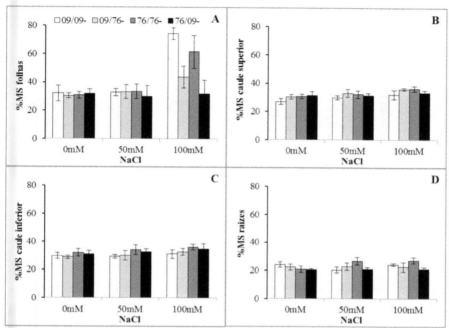

Figure 07. Percentage of dry mass of leaves (A), upper stem (B), lower stem (C), roots (D) of grafted early dwarf cashew plants, subjected to 0, 50 and 100 mM NaCl treatments, observed at 15 and 30 days after the onset of stress (DAE).

With regard to relative water content, it was observed that in the CCP76/CCP76 autograft there was an increase in the control dose up to 50mM and from that point onwards there was a drastic reduction in the 100mM dose. The CCP09/CCP09 autograft showed an increase from the 50mM dose onwards. The percentage of membrane damage for grafts CCP09/CCP76, CCP76/CCP76 and CCP76/CCP09 showed a gradual decrease as the salt concentration increased, while for autograft CCP09/CCP09 there was a reduction up to the 50mM dose and from there onwards there was an increase up to 100mM (Figure 08).

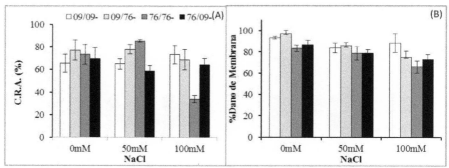

Figure 08. Relative water content (A) and membrane damage (B) of grafted early dwarf cashew plants subjected to 0, 50 and 100 mM NaCl treatments, observed at 15 and 30 days after the onset of stress (DAT).

The salt treatments caused drastic changes in the content of Na^+, K^+ and Ca^{+2} ions in the leaves (Figure 09). Possibly, there were no differences in the accumulation of Na^+ between plants treated with 50 and 100mM NaCl. However, plants treated with 100mM NaCl suffered a reduction in K+ content, especially seedlings CCP09/CCP09, CCP09/ CCP76 and CCP76/CCP09. In addition, the salt treatment caused an increase in Ca^{+2} content, especially for CCP09/CCP76 and CCP76/CCP76 seedlings.

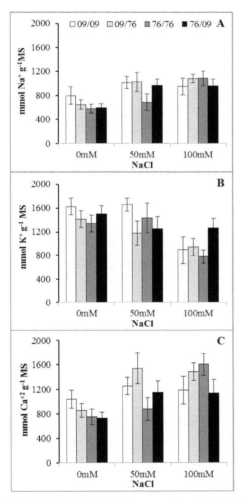

Figure 09. Na$^+$ (A), K$^+$ (B) and Ca^{+2} (C) content of grafted early dwarf cashew plants subjected to 0, 50 and 100 mM NaCl treatments, observed at 15 and 30 days after the onset of stress (DAE).

2.5. FINAL CONSIDERATIONS

Early dwarf cashew seedlings subjected to salt treatments with 50 and 100mM NaCl showed obvious damage and different response patterns in relation to the parameters analysed. It is possible to see differences between the seedlings by analysing the percentage of leaf moisture, relative leaf water content, percentage of

41

leaf dry mass, leaf area, number of leaves and content of Na ions$^+$, K$^+$ and Ca^{+2}. In addition, according to the variables analysed, the CCP09/CCP76 seedlings and especially CCP76/CCP09 were less affected by the salt treatments than the other seedling combinations.

2.6. BIBLIOGRAPHICAL REFERENCES

ALMEIDA, J.I.L.; ARAÚJO, F.E.; BARROS, L.M. **Characteristics of the EPACE CL 49 cashew clone**. EPACE, 1992. p. 160-165. (Annual Research Report 1980/1992).

BANULS, J.; PRIMO-MILLO, E. Effects of chloride and sodium on gas exchange parameters and water relations of Citrus plants. **Physiologia Plantarum**, v.85, p. 115-123,1995.

BARROS, L. de M. et al. **Technical recommendations for growing early dwarf cashew trees**. Fortaleza: EMBRAPA-CNPAT, 1993. 65p.

BARROS, L. M. Origin and Geographical Distribution. In: LIMA, V. P. M. S. **A cultura do cajueiro no Nordeste do Brasil**. Fortaleza: BNB/ETENE, 1998 p.321-355 (Economic and Social Studies Series, 35).

BARROS, M. L.; CAVALCANTI, J. J.; PAIVA, J. R. Selection of dwarf cashew clones for commercial planting in the state of Ceará. **Pesquisa Agropecuária Brasileira**, v.11, p. 2197-2204, 2000.

BONHERT, H. J., JENSEN, R. G. Metabolic engineering for increased salt tolerancethe next step. **Australian Journal Plant Physiology**, vol 23, 661-666, 1996.

EMATER-RN, **SAPE AND BNB sign partnership for investments in cashew cultivation in West Potiguar,** Available at: http://goo.gl/G4qcp. Accessed on: May 2013.

ESTAN, M. T.; MARTINEZ-RODRIGUES, M. M.; PEREZ-ALFOCEA, F.; FLOWERS, T. J.; BOLARIN, M. C. Grafting raises the salt tolerance of tomato through limiting the transport of sodium and chloride to the shoot. **Journal of Experimental Botany**, v. 56, n. 412, p.703-712, 2005.

FAGERIA, N. K.; GHEYI, H.R. Genetic improvement of crops and selection of cultivars. P. 363-383. In: **Management and control of salinity in irrigated agriculture**. XVI Brazilian Congress of Agricultural Engineering. 1997.

FERREIRA-SILVA, S. L.; SILVA, E.N.; CARVALHO, F. E. L.; LIMA, C.S.; ALVES, F.A.L.; SILVEIRA, J.A.G. Physiological alterations modulated by rootstock and scion combination in cashew under salinity, **Scientia Horticulturae**, v. 127, p.39-45, 2010.

FERREIRA-SILVA, S. L.; VOIGT, E. L.; VIÉGAS, R. A.; PAIVA, J. R.; SILVEIRA, J. A. G. Influence of rootstocks on the resistance of cashew seedlings to salt stress. **Pesquisa Agropecuária Brasileira**, v. 44, n. 4, p. 361-367, 2009.

HOAGLAND, D.R.; ARNON, D. I. **The water culture method for growing plants without soils**. Berkeley: California Agricultural Experimental Station, 347p., 1950.

IBGE. **Systematic survey of agricultural production - 2011 harvest**, Available at: http://www.ibge.gov.br. Accessed on: May 2013.

IRIGOYEN, J. J.; EMERICH, D.W.; SÁNCHEZ-DÍAZ, M. Water stress induced changes in concentrations of proline and total soluble sugars in nodulated alfalfa (Medicago sativa) plants. **Physiologia Plantarum**, v. 84, p.67-72, 1992.

LUTTS, S.; KINET, J.; BOUHARMONT, J. NaCl induced senescence in leaves of rice (Oryza sativa) cultivars differing in salinity resistance. **Annals of Botany,** v. 78, p.389-398, 1996.

MALAVOLTA, E.; VITTI, G. C.; OLIVEIRA, S. A. de. **Evaluation of plant nutritional status: principles and applications**. 2.ed. Piracicaba: POTAFOS, 1997. 319p.

MURTHY, K. N.; KUMAR, K. V., BHAGAVAN, S. et al. A rapid non-destructive method of estimating leaf area in cashew. **Acta Horticulturae**, 108: 46-48,1985.

PARAÍBA, **Rômulo receives IFAD mission and discusses financing for agriculture,** Available at: http://goo.gl/Wi8Fv. Accessed on: May 2013.

PONTE, L.F.A., FERREIRA, O.S., ALVES, F.A.L., FERREIRA-SILVA, S.L., PEREIRA, V.L.A., SILVEIRA, J.A.G. Variability of physiological indicators of resistance to salinity among dwarf and giant cashew genotypes. **Pesq. agropec. bras.**, Brasília, v.46, n.1, p.1-8, jan. 2011.

REVISTA FIEC, **For the chestnut**. Available at: http://goo.gl/etjy7. Accessed on: May 2013.